This book belongs to

....

AUTUMN
PUBLISHING

Published in 2021
First published in the UK by Autumn Publishing
An imprint of Igloo Books Ltd
Cottage Farm, NN6 0BJ, UK
Owned by Bonnier Books
Sveavägen 56, Stockholm, Sweden
www.autumnpublishing.co.uk

Copyright © 2021 Autumn Publishing

1121 001
2 4 6 8 10 9 7 5 3 1
ISBN 978-1-80108-238-9

Wildlife consultant: David Winnard

Illustrated by Amelia Herbertson
Written by Marnie Willow

Designed by Chris Stanley
Edited by Helen Catt

The publisher would like to thank Claire Sipi for
proofreading and Elizabeth Wise for the index.

Printed and manufactured in China.

How to Find a

Unicorn

AUTUMN
PUBLISHING

Contents

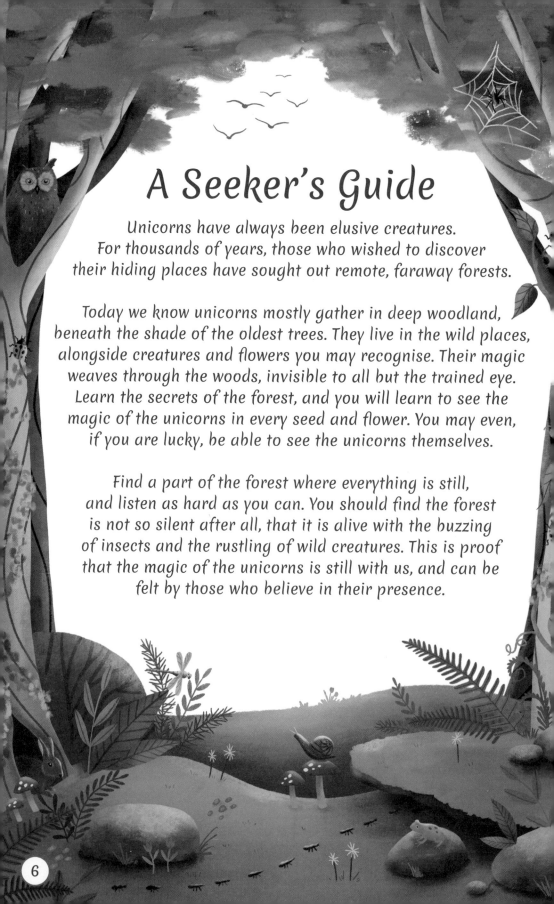

A Seeker's Guide

Unicorns have always been elusive creatures.
For thousands of years, those who wished to discover
their hiding places have sought out remote, faraway forests.

Today we know unicorns mostly gather in deep woodland,
beneath the shade of the oldest trees. They live in the wild places,
alongside creatures and flowers you may recognise. Their magic
weaves through the woods, invisible to all but the trained eye.
Learn the secrets of the forest, and you will learn to see the
magic of the unicorns in every seed and flower. You may even,
if you are lucky, be able to see the unicorns themselves.

Find a part of the forest where everything is still,
and listen as hard as you can. You should find the forest
is not so silent after all, that it is alive with the buzzing
of insects and the rustling of wild creatures. This is proof
that the magic of the unicorns is still with us, and can be
felt by those who believe in their presence.

A Year's Cycle

Unicorns are present at all times of year, but as the year waxes and wanes, the way their magic is imprinted on their surroundings changes. If you can recognise the signs at different times of year, you will greatly increase your chances of tracking down unicorns.

A reflection caught in an icy mirror

A silvery strand of a unicorn's mane

Deep winter

Early spring

Hoofprints in the snow

Early winter

Late spring

Crystal dewdrops

Shadows in the mist

Late autumn

Early summer

A scattering of rainbow petals

Early autumn

High summer

A gilded leaf

A perfect rose

Safe Seeking

A successful seeker is a prepared seeker. Be cautious; it is wise not to venture out alone unless you are a highly seasoned traveller. Even the most experienced travellers always tell their comrades where they are going and when they expect to return. You may find some of the equipment below useful for your quest.

Drinks and snacks

Unicorns may be able to live solely off the fruits of the forest and morning dew, but explorers need sustanance. Always make sure you have adequate supplies for your mission.

Map and compass

Knowing the lay of the land will help you navigate to the deepest parts of the forest, where unicorns are most likely to be found – not to mention helping you find your way safely out again.

Binoculars

Unicorns, like many woodland creatures, are cautious around humans. Find a quiet shelter or hiding place and use binoculars to watch from a distance.

Outdoor clothing

Hot sun, rain, snow, mud, prickly branches and stinging nettles are all perils an adventurer may face. Check the weather before you go out and dress accordingly.

The Seeker's Code

Unicorns have a deep sense of respect for the natural world. Those who wish to find them must do as well. Follow this code when out in the countryside. Above all, always remember the golden rule.

1. Take your litter home with you if you can't find a bin.

2. Only pick wild plants if there are plenty growing, and just pick a few.

3. Don't pick rare plants and never uproot plants without permission.

4. Never disturb nesting birds or steal birds' eggs.

5. Be gentle with any wild creatures you come across. Never take them away from where you found them.

The Golden Rule:
Leave things in the wild as you found them.

Never-near plants

In every forest, there are plants and trees that unicorns never go close to and that seekers should steer clear of – the never-near plants. These are plants that sting or itch or are dangerous in other ways. Here are some to be aware of, but every forest is different. Make sure you know how to spot the never-near plants specific to any place before you go exploring.

Hemlock

This plant is deadly poisonous to eat. It smells bad, like a rodent, and has purple blotches on the stem.

Stinging nettle

The leaves and stems of stinging nettles are covered in tiny needle-like spines. Their sting is itchy and painful.

Hemlock water-dropwort

This posionous plant looks a lot like hemlock, except it doesn't have the purple blotches on the stem. It grows near water and on riverbanks.

Poison oak

This is a trailing vine or a small shrub, not a tree like 'true' oak, even though its leaves look similar. The sap causes a nasty rash. Be careful not to touch it if walking through places where it grows.

Giant hogweed

This plant can grow several metres tall. The sap in its hollow stems causes burns and blisters.

Poison ivy

Much like poison oak, this plant grows as a trailing vine or a small shrub, and can cause a rash if touched. Make sure to cover up well when walking nearby.

Poison sumac

This plant grows as a small tree or a tall shrub in some boggy, wet woodland. It is recognisable by its bunches of between seven and thirteen smooth, thin leaves. Brushing up against it can cause an itchy, painful rash.

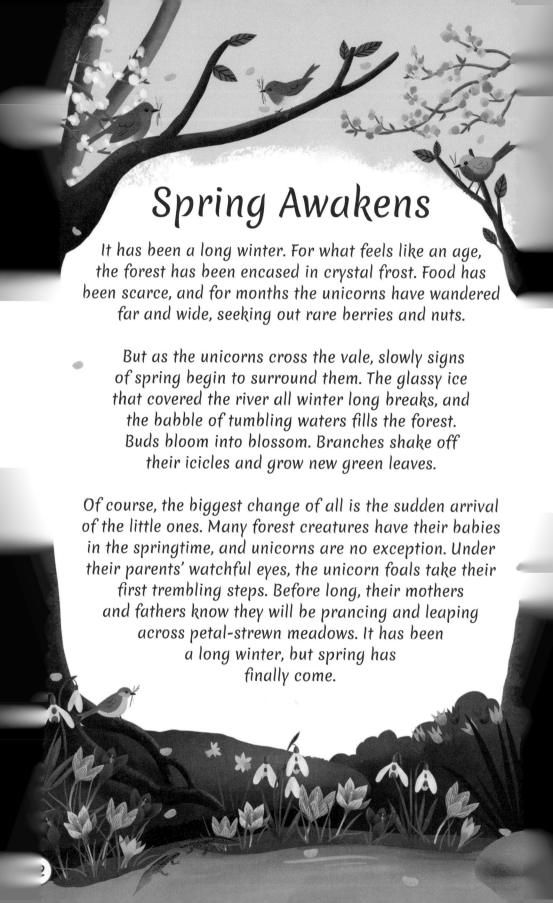

Spring Awakens

It has been a long winter. For what feels like an age, the forest has been encased in crystal frost. Food has been scarce, and for months the unicorns have wandered far and wide, seeking out rare berries and nuts.

But as the unicorns cross the vale, slowly signs of spring begin to surround them. The glassy ice that covered the river all winter long breaks, and the babble of tumbling waters fills the forest. Buds bloom into blossom. Branches shake off their icicles and grow new green leaves.

Of course, the biggest change of all is the sudden arrival of the little ones. Many forest creatures have their babies in the springtime, and unicorns are no exception. Under their parents' watchful eyes, the unicorn foals take their first trembling steps. Before long, their mothers and fathers know they will be prancing and leaping across petal-strewn meadows. It has been a long winter, but spring has finally come.

Signs of Spring

Unicorn foals are born at the very start of spring, but are all but impossible to spot. You will improve your chances if you stay attuned to the change of season. These are some of the signs that spring is coming.

Snowdrops

These tiny white flowers are often the very first to appear in spring. A late cold snap can leave their tiny heads bobbing above the snow. But, like the unicorn foals they herald, they are hardy little things and the cold doesn't worry them.

Nesting birds

Keep your eyes on the skies and high branches in early spring, and you will see wild birds hard at work. They gather twigs to build nests, and seek soft sheep's wool to make them comfortable for their tiny hatchlings.

Catkins

In early spring, before any trees are in leaf, you may see the branches dripping with catkins. Also known as lamb's tails, catkins are clusters of tiny flowers. The pollen they produce is one of the earliest spring foods for bees and unicorns.

Bluebell shoots

In light, airy parts of the forest, the dull earth can suddenly burst into a thick carpet of green. The flowers won't bloom until the weather is warmer, but their fresh shoots are a sign that spring has arrived. Unicorns never tread on these shoots – they know how delicate and precious they are.

Dawn chorus

There is no surer sign of spring than to hear the calls and songs of birds as the sun rises. The dappled light that falls through fresh new leaves wakes the birds, who begin to sing all at once. Unicorns are born at the very first golden glow of morning, and the dawn chorus is the first thing a newborn unicorn hears when it enters the world.

A Seeker's Wand

Not all seekers use wands, but those that do find them invaluable. A wand may not be taken from the forest, only given by it. Twigs broken from trees by human hands hold no magical properties. Search the ground to find the parts to make your wand. It should feel comfortable when you hold it – you will know when you have found the wand meant for you.

Oak

The strongest of the forest wood, an oak wand will give you courage in the face of adversity.

Goat willow

A gentle wand, especially if you can find a piece with the soft, white catkins still attached.

Rowan

The shiny, grey twigs from the rowan tree make wands known for their strong protective properties.

Ash

This flexible wood's pale bark and dark knots bring the power of light and shade for seeking unicorns at all times of day.

Feathers

Swift as a sparrow, quick
as a hawk. Call the magic
of the birds onto your
side by adding feathers
to your wand.

Petals

Colourful petals will catch
the eye of passing unicorns
and make you known as a
friend. Large petals can be
wrapped around your
wand as stripes.

Fluffy seeds

As they wave in the wind,
these seeds will call to
young unicorns, who love
their gentle softness.

Forest Babies

Unicorns aren't the only animals to give birth in the spring. Hide somewhere quiet, or build a den so you can keep watch from a distance. Make sure you never disturb young creatures.

Deer fawns

While fawns are very young, their mothers leave them in a safe, hidden place while they graze. If you find one, be very quiet and don't go close.

Thrush chicks

Baby birds of all types sit and wait for their parents to fly back to the nest. As soon as the grown-up bird returns, a seeker might hear the squeaking cries as the chicks beg for food.

Fox cubs

While adult foxes scavenge for food, young cubs stay close to the den. In a few weeks, they'll follow their parents around as they learn how to hunt, but for now, they spend their time playing.

Long-eared owl chicks

In spring, it can be easier to spot young owlets than to find the adults. Once they get too big for the nest, they sit out on branches until they're big enough to fly.

Squirrel kits

After just a few weeks, baby squirrels follow their parents out of the drey (nest) to practise scurrying over high branches. If they get tired, their mother might carry them back to the drey on her back.

Rabbit kittens

Newborn rabbits, or kittens, are born with their eyes closed, just like dogs and cats. But soon after their eyes open, just a few weeks after being born, they start exploring the forest on their own.

Tadpoles

Hatched from jelly-like frogspawn, these wriggly creatures are found in shallow rivers and rocky pools at the edges of lakes. Over the next few weeks, they'll grow legs and become little froglets.

Unicorn foals

Of course, all seekers will be watching out for young unicorn foals. Though playful with their friends, they are very shy around strangers, and their parents will sometimes cast cloaking magic over them, so they can't be seen. Be very quiet and look for the part of the forest with the softest grass and the most colourful wildflowers, and you may be able to sense their presence.

Woodland Crowns

These crowns have been made by seekers as gifts for centuries, as thanks to the unicorns for looking after the forest, and as a way to help unicorns channel their power. It is wise to make matching crowns for the unicorns and for yourself, so the unicorns can easily find you among the trees.

Daisy coronet

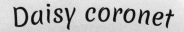

Use your fingernails to push slits into the stems of daisies. Slide the stem of the next daisy through the slit. Keep going to make a chain that winds around to make a coronet.

To join up the ends, make an extra slit in the last stem and carefully push the head of the first daisy through to make a button to hold the coronet together.

You can use other wildflowers to make crowns, such as...

...dandelions...

... or clover.

Goosegrass garland

Goosegrass has stems covered in tiny hooks, which means it sticks to itself. Bunch it together to make a crown shape, then weave in other flowers to decorate it.

Make sure you don't pick rare or poisonous plants.

The bravest and boldest unicorns will choose the

feather crown.

Make a circle from a long, bendy willow stem, weaving the ends over and under each other to keep them in place. Wrap more willow stems around the circle. Push the quills of found feathers through the gaps between the stems.

Hang the finished crown on a low branch or place it by the base of a tree for unicorns to find.

Birds of the Forest

As spring gets under way, a quiet and careful seeker is sure to spot flurries of wings between the branches, or catch sudden birdsong on the breeze. Woodland that is frequented by lots of different birds is likely to be visited by unicorns, too, so keep a weather eye on the skies.

Redpoll

These little brown and red birds often perch or hang upside-down near alder or birch catkins in cool weather.

Goldcrest

Look for a flash of yellow, flitting around the tree. This tiny bird forages constantly for bugs and grubs to eat.

Wren

These tiny, noisy birds hide in bushes and scrub. They're tricky to spot, but easy to hear. Listen for a jumbled, burbling, chirruping call.

Pheasant

These ground-dwelling birds build nests called 'scrapes' in the undergrowth. When startled, they launch upwards with a loud flapping and croaking cry – an alarm call to other birds and any nearby unicorns.

Crow

These clever, fearless birds are good at recognising individual seekers and unicorns. A seeker who does a favour for a crow may find that favour repaid in future.

Magpie

If you see one magpie, there are likely to be others nearby. They're fond of glittering, secret treasures. If you are lucky, you may find their little troves hidden in the undergrowth.

Treecreeper

These little birds scurry up the trees like mice. They are tiny and quick, so a seeker needs sharp eyes to spot them.

Scarlet phoenix

Only a few fortunate seekers have ever spotted this elusive bird. Keep an eye out for signs of its presence: scorch marks on a tree branch, or a crimson feather on the breeze.

Into Summer

Ever so slowly, the days become longer
and the sun begins to shine more warmly.
The forest is busy with life; bees and butterflies
collect nectar from summer flowers and squirrels
forage for green hazelnuts in the trees. Unicorn foals,
so unsteady on their feet just a few months ago,
now confidently canter across fields and forest,
leaving whirlwinds of petals dancing in their wake.

Food is easy to find in summer for many forest animals,
and unicorns are no exception; there are lush meadow
grasses peppered with daisies, early-ripening fruits
and rich berries like jewels in the hedgerows. With
food plentiful, summer is a season of long, lazy days.
Older unicorns lie on grassy banks, enjoying the warmth of
the golden sunlight, while the younger ones play. Their
joyful whinnies carry on the wind for miles around.

On the hottest days of the year, even unicorns must
seek shelter in cool groves and by rivers and streams,
away from the beating heat of the sun. And older unicorns
know that a spell of very hot days often means
a summer storm is on its way...

Butterflies

At the edges of the woodland and in clearings, dappled green rays break into sudden golden sun. There, swirls of dancing butterflies can be seen, their wings shimmering and flashing in the light. A quiet and careful seeker may be able to get quite close to a butterfly resting on a blade of long grass. If they are very still and peaceful, a butterfly may even land upon them.

Red admiral

They may be small, but red admirals are bold. They lay their eggs among stinging nettles, so predators can't get close to the caterpillars without being stung. As adults, they often flutter close to humans, even landing on those they truly trust.

Small white

This delicate butterfly has simple white wings with black speckles. They're keen on blue and yellow flowers, so keep watch in wildflower meadows.

Painted lady

These tortoiseshell butterflies migrate in large groups, so if you see one, you'll probably find lots nearby. On sunny days, they prefer open flower meadows, but when it's cooler, they stay close to the ground in dips and hollows.

Small copper

Touch your index finger to your thumb to make a circle – this is the size of a small copper. They can fly very quickly, but prefer to spend a lot of their time basking on warm, sunny rocks.

Tiny meadowdancer

Barely visible to the human eye, these miniature butterflies are easy to miss. They thrive in groves and flower meadows that are under the protection of unicorns, and clouds of them often follow unicorn foals around as they play.

Summer Flowers

Summer brings a riot of wildflowers. Some, like honeysuckle and dogroses, ramble over trees. Others stand up straight from the ground in sunny clearings, a flash of colour in the green grass. Keep an eye out for these flowers – they are particular favourites of unicorns.

Elderflower

As spring just begins to turn to summer, elderflowers appear like lace on tall shrubs. Their tiny white and champagne-coloured petals can be used to make a sweet cordial, but unicorns love to graze elderflowers straight from the tree.

Wild dogroses

These pale pink wildflowers first appear in early summer. Their clambering stems scramble over trees and hedgerows. As the flowers die back, they leave rich red rosehips, a late summer treat for unicorns that can last right into winter time.

Foxgloves

The tall stems of these flowers can grow as tall as a unicorn. Unicorns know that these beautiful bell-like flowers are poisonous, and are just for looking, not for touching.

Honeysuckle

These sweet-smelling flowers bloom in the late afternoon and evening, filling the woods with their fragrance. Young unicorn foals like to suck the honey-sweet nectar from the freshly picked flowers.

Eleganza unicornica

This flower is almost completely see-through. One can only glimpse its petals when a ray of golden sunlight falls upon it on the hottest day of the year. The lucky seeker will see a burst of irridescent sparkles. Unicorns do not eat this flower, but its rich, heady scent has healing properties that help replenish a unicorn's magic.

By the River

Riverbeds make safe havens for lots of different animals. Unicorns usually visit the river to drink, but on hot summer days they may spend a while playing in the shallows.

Otter

Look out at dawn and dusk for this sleek, furry animal gliding through the water to catch fish, or perching by the water's edge.

Canada goose

Canada geese are noisy birds, especially around sunrise and sunset. In late summer, large groups of them can be seen flying in a V-shape as they begin their long migration south for the winter.

Mayflies

For most of their lives, these flies live as tiny nymphs hidden among the underwater plants at the river's edge. But for one day, they grow lace-like wings and dart across the surface of the water laying their eggs.

Grey heron

These tall birds wade in the water or stand on the riverbanks, often balancing on one leg so they can move quickly to catch fish in their long bills.

Mallard

Male mallards have bottle-green feathers on their heads, while female mallards are speckled brown. They dabble their beaks in the water to catch bugs and graze on pondweed.

Rainbow trout

This freshwater fish can be recognised by the shimmering pink stripe along its body. They lay their eggs in shallow pools. These eggs hatch into tiny fish called fingerlings.

A Seeker's Hide

Seekers' work is often best done in secret, hidden
from the view of forest creatures. This way, unicorns and
other animals can carry on their woodland business
without being disturbed. Smart seekers build hides
out of fallen branches and leaves, where they can
wait and watch for whatever might appear.

Be extra careful with heavy sticks. Drag them
rather than carry them, and make sure
they're securely lodged in your den
so they don't fall and hurt you.

A sturdy tree with
a low horizontal
branch makes
a good base
for a hide.

Remember, a seeker never damages trees or animals' homes.

Lean sticks against large tree trunks to create a den.

For smaller trunks, lean sticks all around the outside, like a wigwam.

A large fallen tree can make a good base for a mini hide.

Summer Fruits

As the summer reaches hedgerows drip with rich red berries, while tree branches are heavy with fruit. When food is this plentiful, unicorns can wander lazily through the woods, eating from stems and branches as they pass.

> ⚠ **Warning:** some berries are dangerous. Never eat anything you find unless an adult has said it's safe.

Wild Strawberries

Almost as elusive as unicorns themselves, wild strawberries are the favourite food of unicorn foals. The plants grow low against the ground, creeping in hedgerows, on heaths and in open woodland. They are best picked on warm summer days, when the sunshine has made them extra sweet.

Blackberries

Blackberries grow in most forests on straggly, spiky canes and great, big bushes. Unicorns will eat an entire bushful in one go, if the birds don't get to them first.

Raspberries

You can find these berries in rocky woodland, growing on tall, prickly canes. Be careful not to confuse them with unripe blackberries, which are too sour for unicorns. Their stalks are straighter and more slender than blackberries, and have finer spines.

Wild Apples

In the sheltered edges of the forest, you may be lucky enough to find a wild apple tree. The fruits come in colours from sunset gold to ruby red. Taller unicorns bend the high branches down so smaller unicorns can reach the fruit.

Burning Hazebelle

Only unicorns can eat this rare and unique fruit. Be sure not to pick it if you find it, but leave it for them. It is ripe on only one day a year, the hottest day of high summer. If you are lucky enough to find it on this day, a unicorn is sure to be watching.

Reading the Sky

Keep an eye on the horizon. Seekers can go out in most weathers, as long as they are prepared. Unicorns, too, will watch the skies, heading for shelter when there are signs of heavy rain, and hiding completely away in the run-up to a thunderstorm.

Altostratus

These light grey, dull clouds stretch into the distance without changing. Be ready for a light drizzle when these clouds are in the sky, but they shouldn't put off more adventurous seekers.

Cumulus

Fluffy, cotton-wool clouds mean the weather should stay fine. Seekers should watch these clouds for messages between unicorns.

Look for shapes in the clouds; unicorns hide hearts, stars and flowers to let their friends know they have found a safe haven.

Cirrus

White, wispy clouds high in the sky are a sign of a fair day for seeking. Unicorn magic is extra strong on these days.

Cirrocumulus

Sometimes called 'mackerel sky' because of their fish-scale appearance, these clouds can sometimes be a sign of a change in the weather.

Nimbostratus

This thick, low blanket of grey cloud usually means rain is on the way. Seekers should be prepared.

Cumulonimbus

When these dark, towering stormclouds fill the sky, unicorns find shelter, as should all wise seekers.

Woodland Trees

After the spring blossom has fallen, the trees
are cloaked in shades of green, and unicorns
wander in the sun-dappled shade. Unicorns
know each tree of a forest individually:
their names, shapes, scents and stories.

Horse chestnuts

As its name might suggest, this
tree is popular with unicorns.
It spreads its branches wide,
making a broad, flat-bottomed
canopy. In autumn, it drops
shining conkers, treasures for
seekers and unicorns.

Maple

This tall, slender tree is
known for its five-pointed
leaves. Its sweet sap can be
boiled down to make maple
syrup, and is a favourite
of young unicorns.

Pine

This cone-shaped evergreen is covered in needles. Unlike many trees, it stays green all year around. Its needles and sap have a sharp smell that attracts unicorns from a long way away.

Oak

The oak tree's leafy, bunched-up layers make homes for lots of animals. Squirrels scamper in its branches, birds nest in its canopy, foxes make dens in its hollows, while spiders and butterflies live in its nooks and crannies.

Rowan

The glistening red berries of this tree are a favourite of moths, bees and blackbirds. Unicorns will rest at rowan trees to restore their strength.

Willow

The long, trailing branches of this tree make a perfect place for both seekers and unicorns to take shelter from the summer sun.

Silver birch

This tree gets its name from its silvery, papery bark. Seekers often write messages to the forest's unicorns upon any peelings of birch bark they find on the ground.

Like deers' newly grown antlers, baby unicorns' horns are velvety to the touch. Deers and unicorns rub their heads against rough tree bark to remove this velvet coating, leaving marks on trees.

Ancient Trees

In each forest, there is one tree that is older than all others around it. The magic that flows from this tree is deeply potent. Several times a year, unicorns will make their way to this tree to pay their respects. Finding the most ancient tree can be tricky, but there are several things to look out for while out on your quest.

Mushrooms and other fungi.

Knobbles, knots and warty lumps.

Thick, gnarled bark.

Deep hollows in the trunk.

A fat trunk, too wide to get your arms around.

Fallen branches around its base.

Autumn's Glow

It felt like summer would last forever, with its glorious long, golden afternoons. But as the gold summer light gets richer and deeper, it is clear that autumn is on its way.

As mornings in the forest become shrouded with mist, and the evenings become cooler and darker, the hedgerows burst into fruit in one last determined, harvest before the winter. Squirrels collect ripe nuts for their winter stores, while unicorns forage for sweet apples on the ground.

The unicorns that were born in the spring are now fiercely independent, galloping beneath a canopy of leaves alight with reds, oranges and ochres. This is the time of year when a seeker is most likely to find a lone unicorn, as they blaze their own paths in search of new adventures. They will not leave their families yet, but they are testing the boundaries in preparation. They will not forget the seekers they encounter and the friends they make in this time.

Autumn Leaves

As autumn draws closer, leaves turn red and fall from the trees. Recognising their leaves will help you to identify different trees. It will also enable you to spot leaves that have travelled a long way, a sign that unicorn magic is strong in that area.

Willow

Long, smooth and slender, these finger-like leaves grow evenly spaced on flexible twigs. Some willows have leaves with a soft, velvety coating on the underside.

Horse chestnut

Bunches of five or seven tear-drop shape, toothed-edged leaves are joined together at a point, at the end of a short, green stem.

Maple

Maple leaves have five points. They are some of the most colourful leaves of autumn, turning vibrant shades of scarlet and yellow.

Silver birch

The little, triangular, toothed-edged leaves of this tree turn bright yellow in autumn and fall all together in the wind like confetti.

Oak

Oak leaves have rounded bumps and grow in bunches. They often look blotchy as they change colour. When they fall, they make a rich leaf mulch that is home and food to lots of bugs, beetles and fungi.

Evergreen needles

Pine   Spruce   Fir

Pine, spruce and firs all have needles that stay attached to the tree all year round. They can look very similar, but to tell the difference look closely at the needles and how they grow. If they're bunched together with several needles growing from one point, it's a pine. If they grow singly, it's a spruce or a fir. Try rolling a needle between your fingertips. Spruce needles have four sides and roll easily. Fir needles are flat, so won't roll.

Nuts and Seeds

As the autumn light gets deeper, seeds and nuts start to rain from the treetops. If planted deep and left undisturbed for many years, these seeds will grow to be great trees for future unicorns and seekers. But a lot won't make it that far; squirrels and unicorns need feeding now, and a store of autumn nuts can make a long winter feel much shorter.

Acorn

Small seeds in thimble-sized cups hold the potential to become giant oak trees. They change from apple-green to warm brown as they ripen over autumn.

Conkers

The spiky green cases of conkers can be spotted on horse chestnut trees from midsummer, but it takes several weeks for the conkers to become ready. When they do, each green case splits to reveal a dark, glossy nut inside.

Sweet chestnuts

It's easy to confuse sweet chestnuts with conkers. The green cases of sweet chestnuts have finer, denser spikes, like a hedgehog. Inside, you'll find several chestnuts, each with a flat edge and a tassel at the point. Unicorns and squirrels will chew through the hard shell and eat them straight away, but people prefer them roasted.

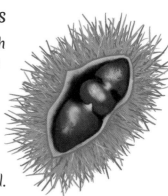

Pine cones

Pine seeds are hidden deep inside a wooden cone. The scales around the outside of the cone can draw in water, so they swell shut and keep the seeds safe inside in wet weather. Once they dry out again, the cone opens up so the seeds can fall and be carried away by the wind.

Hazelnuts

Hazelnuts grow in small clusters on hazel trees, their woody cases turning from green to nut-brown through the season. They are foraged by both unicorns and people. They're also loved by dormice, who eat up a glut of them before they hibernate through the winter.

Maple helicopters

The seeds of maples come in pairs, cased in tissue-paper thin wings that get swept along in the wind. Watch these as they fall – they'll twirl and spiral if unicorns have been nearby.

Dreamtree kernel

This strange nut grows on the very rare dreamtree. It has deep sapphire casing. As autumn deepens, the kernel turns from bright fuschia to shimmering gold. Its magic gives its guardian sweet dreams for a whole winter. Unicorns give them as gifts to those who protect them.

Campfire's Call

Gather around this magical campfire to tell tales of the unicorns.
Real fires in forests can be dangerous, but if a seeker creates this
illusionary fire, imbued with the heat of autumn leaves, unicorns
may draw close and whisper their stories. A seeker who closes
their eyes and follows their imagination may find that they can
hear those stories and tell them to others.

Use short sticks to
build a teepee shape.

Gather a mix of leaves in reds,
oranges and yellows. Arrange
them between the sticks so they
look like flickering flames.

Take a glowstick or LED torch
and place it pointing upwards
in the middle of the fire.

Stories to tell

How unicorns first
came to the forest

Stories of seekers
through history

Tales of unicorns from
around the world

The legend of
the lost unicorn

Collect conkers and
stones and arrange
them in a circle around
your fire's edge.

When you are finished with the campfire, take
the torch and leave the rest as it is. It will
become a home for bugs and beetles.

Forest Fungi

It takes unicorn foals a long time to learn about the different types of fungi in a forest. Similarly, seekers should request advice from more experienced foragers before picking, handling or gathering any found mushrooms.

 Warning: Some mushrooms are deadly poisonous. Always check with an adult before touching any mushroom.

Chanterelle

Unicorns like to eat these egg-yolk yellow mushrooms with frilly edges and gills that run all along the stem. They have a fruity smell, a bit like ripe apricots.

Horn of plenty

These funnel-shaped mushrooms are dark brown or black, and can be tricky to spot amid the leaf litter. If you find one, there will probably be more nearby. They grow in clusters on the forest floor, often in damp places near oak and beech trees.

Penny bun

Look for these mushrooms in light, airy woodland clearings a few days after heavy rain. They have big, fat, bulbous stems and round, dimpled, brown caps that look like fresh bread rolls.

Plums and custard

This mushroom gets its name from its pretty pink speckled cap and custard yellow gills underneath. They grow on rotting wood, especially in evergreen forests.

Shaggy inkcap

When picked, this mushroom collapses into a puddle of ink in just a few hours. Unicorns use this inky black liquid to leave signs to each other around the forest.

Giant puffball

These big, round balls often grow as big as a football, and sometimes much bigger. When they're mature, they detach themselves from the ground and roll around in the breeze, scattering spores.

Hen of the woods

This wrinkly mushroom grows on old trees as a big frilly, feathery clump, close to the ground. They mostly grow on oak trees, especially ones near ponds or rivers.

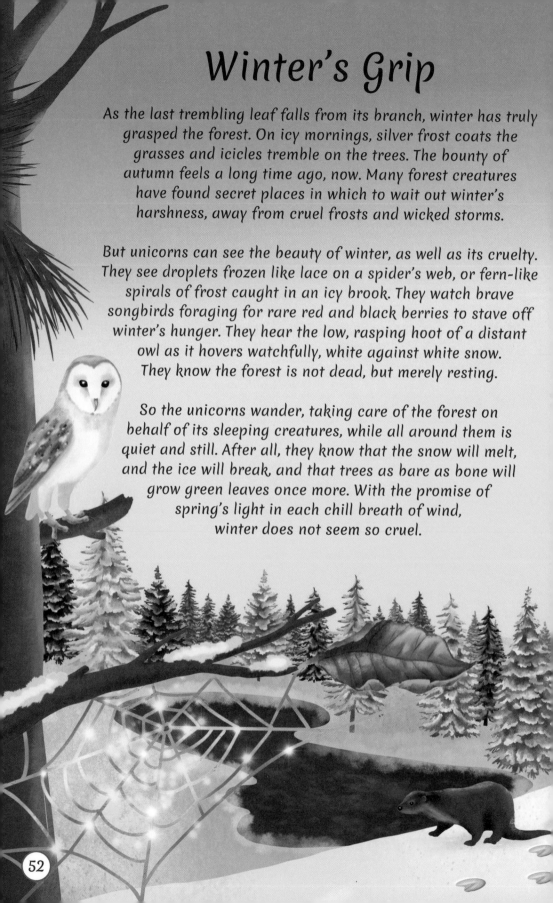

Winter's Grip

As the last trembling leaf falls from its branch, winter has truly grasped the forest. On icy mornings, silver frost coats the grasses and icicles tremble on the trees. The bounty of autumn feels a long time ago, now. Many forest creatures have found secret places in which to wait out winter's harshness, away from cruel frosts and wicked storms.

But unicorns can see the beauty of winter, as well as its cruelty. They see droplets frozen like lace on a spider's web, or fern-like spirals of frost caught in an icy brook. They watch brave songbirds foraging for rare red and black berries to stave off winter's hunger. They hear the low, rasping hoot of a distant owl as it hovers watchfully, white against white snow. They know the forest is not dead, but merely resting.

So the unicorns wander, taking care of the forest on behalf of its sleeping creatures, while all around them is quiet and still. After all, they know that the snow will melt, and the ice will break, and that trees as bare as bone will grow green leaves once more. With the promise of spring's light in each chill breath of wind, winter does not seem so cruel.

Trees in Winter

Telling trees apart in the depths of winter can be tricky. Without their leaves and seeds, it can take an experienced seeker to spot the subtle differences between them. Look at their bark and buds, and you'll come to know them as well as the unicorns do.

Horse chestnuts

Look for big, sticky red-brown buds. The bark is pinky grey on young trees, turning darker and getting more scaley with age.

Silver birch

All year around, this tree is easy to spot thanks to its white bark that peels off on its own in papery sheets. Older trees start to get dark, diamond-shape fissures, especially around the branches.

Sweet chestnut

Look for lines that spiral and swirl around the tree trunk. The slender shoots have ridges running along them, and small copper-coloured buds. There may also be some spiky nut cases left from autumn.

Oak

Oak trees have clusters of buds all together at the end of each twig. Look closely at the buds and you should be able to spot little scales that protect the soft baby leaves. The bark of mature oak trees is hard, grey and deeply ridged, a perfect place for moss to grow, and a safe hiding place for bugs, beetles and spiders.

Hazel

Look for a tree with more than one trunk and smooth silver or copper bark. The bark is shiny on younger trees, getting rougher and more ridged with age. Depending on how far through the winter you are, you may spot catkins dripping from the branches.

Ash

Look for velvety black buds on smooth silver-grey twigs that are bent upwards towards the sky. The bark is smooth and pale grey-beige. In very old trees, it may start to look slightly ridged and bumpy, but much less so than oak.

Winter Berries

Not all the trees are bare of fruit in winter. These late berries provide winter food for birds, who take cover in the evergreen foliage or dense tangle of twigs. Unicorns also graze on some of these berries; you may find telltale hoofprints in the snow nearby.

Holly

The thick, glossy leaves of this bush can be sharp, so seekers should beware. The bright red berries are popular with thrushes and other little songbirds, but unicorns prefer to look rather than eat.

Dogwood

In spring and summer, this shrub is not particularly recognisable, but in winter it comes alive as a flaming crown of red stems, dotted with blue-black or deep purple berries.

Blackthorn

This tree looks remarkably unpromising, with its spiny, dark thorns and small, bruise-black fruits called sloes. Unicorns won't touch the sloes until after the first frost, which breaks the tough skin. After that, it's a feeding frenzy. Humans who are lucky enough to find sloes often use them to make jam or syrup.

Mistletoe

Mistletoe is known for being a parasite that saps strength from its host plant, but the small white berries are ideal food for birds. Unicorns don't eat mistletoe berries, but they do have a tradition of nuzzling each other whenever they pass beneath a mistletoe plant, casting a quiet spell to keep the forest safe for the winter.

Ivy

Tendrils of ivy creep and clamber over taller trees or through hedgerows. Dense and evergreen, this tangle of vines is a hiding place for moths and spiders, whose webs fill it with silken lace, while the berries are food for blackbirds and starlings.

Rosehips

Once the petals fall from the wild roses, the middle of the flower becomes a bright red rosehip. These can appear from late summer onwards, but unicorns will always leave a few through the winter to brighten up darker days.

Shimmershade

This climbing plant only grows on truly ancient trees, clambering high in the branches to make the most of the winter sun. It is too high up to find easily, but its kaleidoscopic berries cast a strange shimmering light onto the forest floor that young unicorns love to play in.

Animal Tracks

Snow and hard, frozen mud preserve the tracks of animals, so a seeker can tell what creatures have passed through the forest in the hours before them. You can preserve tracks in plaster, to keep the crystalline magic of winter with you through the year.

Red fox

Fox prints look a lot like dog prints, with four toes and claws at the front, and a triangular pad at the back. Foxes' toes are closer together than dogs'.

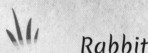

Rabbit

Rabbits' back feet are much longer than their front paws, so you'll see two little prints and two long, thin prints, all grouped close together.

Birds

Little birds like sparrows and thrushes hop, so their footprints come in pairs. Bigger birds, like crows and pheasants, walk, so their footprints alternate left and right.

Deer

Deer hooves leave distinctive splayed prints. Depending on the type and age of the deer that left the prints, they can vary a lot in size.

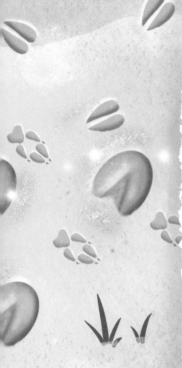

Unicorn

It can be hard to tell unicorn hoofprints from other horses' hoofprints. Look for a tell-tale sparkle in the snow nearby, or for other signs that unicorns have been nearby.

A track for keeps

If a track has been left in firm mud, you can take its imprint.

1 Clip a long strip of card into a circle that fits around the print. Push it into the mud.

2 Mix up some plaster of Paris according to the pack instructions and pour it into the print.

3 Let it set for 15 minutes, then carefully dig up the whole footprint. Wrap it in newspaper to take it somewhere safe and dry.

4 Let it set for a day, then remove the card. Wash the print under running water, using an old toothbrush to scrub it clean. Then decorate it with paint or eco-friendly glitter.

Pebble Spells

Seekers may communicate with unicorns by leaving behind magic messages. This works particularly well in winter, when the unicorns are on the lookout for changes in their landscape. The rain will wash away the chalk and charcoal over time, but fear not. The message will have called to the unicorns before it is lost.

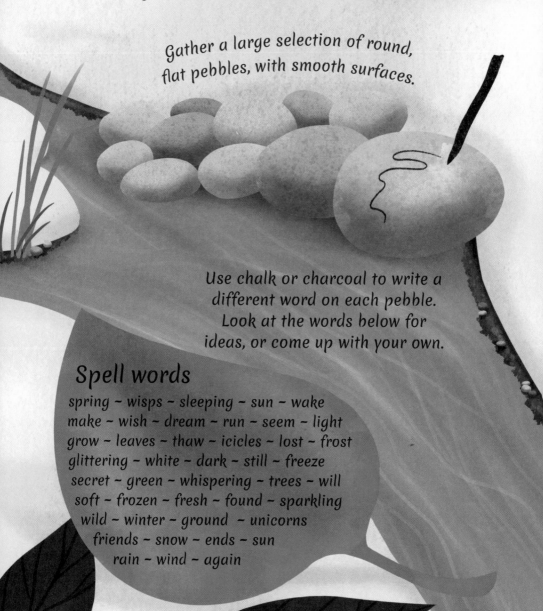

Gather a large selection of round, flat pebbles, with smooth surfaces.

Use chalk or charcoal to write a different word on each pebble. Look at the words below for ideas, or come up with your own.

Spell words

spring ~ wisps ~ sleeping ~ sun ~ wake
make ~ wish ~ dream ~ run ~ seem ~ light
grow ~ leaves ~ thaw ~ icicles ~ lost ~ frost
glittering ~ white ~ dark ~ still ~ freeze
secret ~ green ~ whispering ~ trees ~ will
soft ~ frozen ~ fresh ~ found ~ sparkling
wild ~ winter ~ ground ~ unicorns
friends ~ snow ~ ends ~ sun
rain ~ wind ~ again

Arrange your pebbles in different orders to make up a poem or message to the unicorns.

May winter wake from its sparkling dream
And the forest
green glittering in fresh grow
We seekers wish the woods no ill Through
rain snow and we'll be here still

Winter Windchime

With its thick, low mists, dark evenings and veils of snowstorms, the forest can be hard for the unicorns to navigate in the depths of winter. A seeker may help. The found and fallen things of winter can be gathered together to make a windchime to help unicorns find their way home when all the world is white with snow.

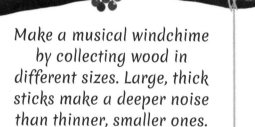

Make a musical windchime by collecting wood in different sizes. Large, thick sticks make a deeper noise than thinner, smaller ones.

Choose a bare, empty branch to hang your windchime so you don't disturb nesting animals.

Decorate the windchimes with pinecones, conkers, bunches of heather and found feathers.

Include rocks and pebbles for a variety of sounds. Try to find ones with holes in so they're easier to tie.

Use natural twine or paper ribbon so it breaks
down naturally when it's no longer needed.

Build a frame by tying twigs
into different shapes, or
hang the pieces of your
windchime directly from
a horizontal branch.

Try tying lots
of short twigs
together.

Forest at Night

Dusk deepens and shadows lengthen as the sun
sets over the trees. For a few brief moments,
the whole forest is set ablaze with fiery
red light, then night falls over the forest.

While baby unicorns sleep soundly in secret,
hidden groves, the adults still keep watch
over their domain. They know the creatures
of the night just as well as they know
the ones that play through the day.

So they listen to the sounds around them;
the chattering of bats and their pups in
the roosts, the call of the owls and
the hum and clicks of the night
insects, while their coats glow
in the midnight shadows,
or sparkle in the silvery
light of the moon.
They know that all
around them is
as it should be.

Night's Creatures

After the sun sets, the creatures of daylight hide away, and instead the nocturnal wildlife comes out of the shadows. Many of the night animals are very sensitive to light – using a torch with a red lens or wrapping the torch in red plastic film can help to make sure they aren't disturbed.

Barn Owl
This owl's heart-shaped face concentrates sounds so it can hear the scratches of mice in snow. The owl can then swoop and catch its prey with pinpoint accuracy.

Glow worm
These beetles glow at night. Look for them in hedgerows or in long grass in woodland clearings.

Stag Beetle
These giant beetles are quite lazy in the day. But after dusk, they clamber over twigs and fly inelegantly in search of other stag beetles.

Bat

Bats fly in quick, swooping paths, catching and eating insects mid-flight. Unable to see clearly, they find their prey by clicking and squeaking, then listening for echoes that bounce back.

Fox

Foxes live in groups called skulks or packs, but they go out alone at night to hunt. When there are pups to look after, other members of the pack bring back food for them.

Woodcock

Usually camouflaged by their brown, speckled feathers, these nocturnal, ground-dwelling birds fly into the air in a zig-zag pattern when they're disturbed.

Celestial Hoofprints

If you go out to the forest on a calm, clear night, and search the skies above, you may see signs of ancient unicorns and other mythical horses. Some of these, Moneceros, Pegasus and Equuleus, have been marked as constellations by generations of seekers past. Some, perhaps, you may be the first to find.

To find Monoceros, look for the three stars of Orion's belt and follow their line to the left of Orion.

Monoceros the unicorn

Orion the hunter

Lepus the rabbit

Cassiopeia the queen

Orion and Cassiopeia are often two of the brightest constellations in the sky. Finding them may help you locate the horses.

There are maps of constellations for all corners of the world, and for all times of the year. Seekers may wish to find a map that is best suited to their needs.

Pegasus the winged horse

Monoceros and Equuleus twinkle only very faintly. A telescope may aid you in your search.

Equuleus the foal

Dawn Rises

At the end of every night, there comes the light of dawn.
For millennia, unicorns have watched the sun rise over
their woodland home, and they will do so for millennia
more, as long as the trees around them stand.

A seeker may go a whole lifetime and never catch more than a
glimpse of a unicorn, a silvery shape caught in the corner of their
eye on a midnight walk, or the flick of a tail far ahead of them
between the trees. But that does not mean their quest is futile.
Unicorns sense those who seek them, and weave their magic
around them, just as they do with all the trees and creatures
of the forest. The true gift of the unicorns and their chosen
comrades is the deep love of all that grows and flourishes.

So, seeker, find a sunrise. Feel its warm glow and its
promise of new beginnings, and know that somewhere,
maybe somewhere very close, there is a unicorn
who is sharing that moment with you.

A Seeker's Notebook

Use these pages to keep a record of the things you find on your explorations. You could write notes of all you hear, take a rubbing of the bark of an ancient tree or stick a fallen leaf onto the page. If you are lucky and keep very still, you may even see a unicorn so calm that you can sketch it here.

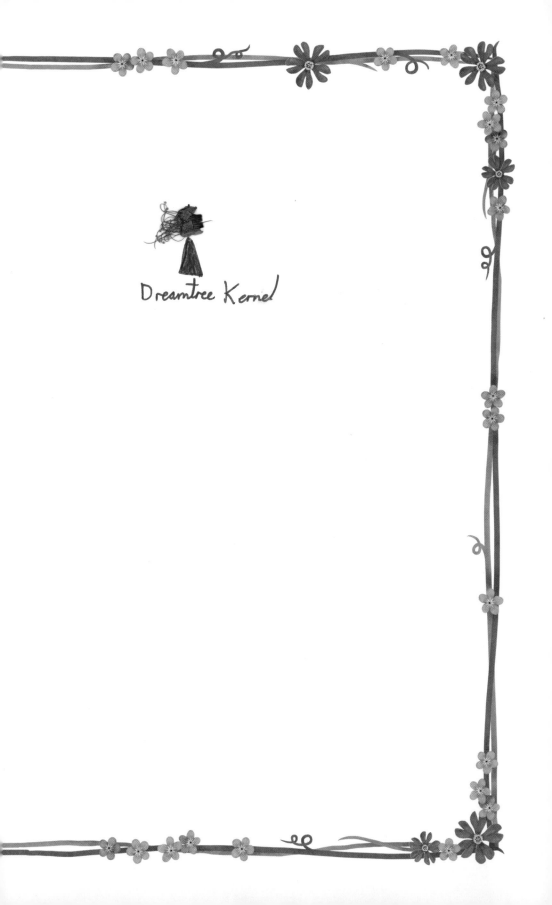

Dreamtree Kernel

Sparkling ground
Snowy dream
May the forest sleep in peace
And us seekers watch
And wish no ill
Make us see
The wishing mill

Wisps of silver
Soft as mane
The sleeping sun...
May rise again
The frozen ice from a tree
The whispering trees, stay young and green
The secret green
Where, oaks been
          Fresh

The unicorns dream
This is me
The lost world of Spring
Can be seen
The dew on the green
Can be seen

So look at sunrise, and I know, this is me.

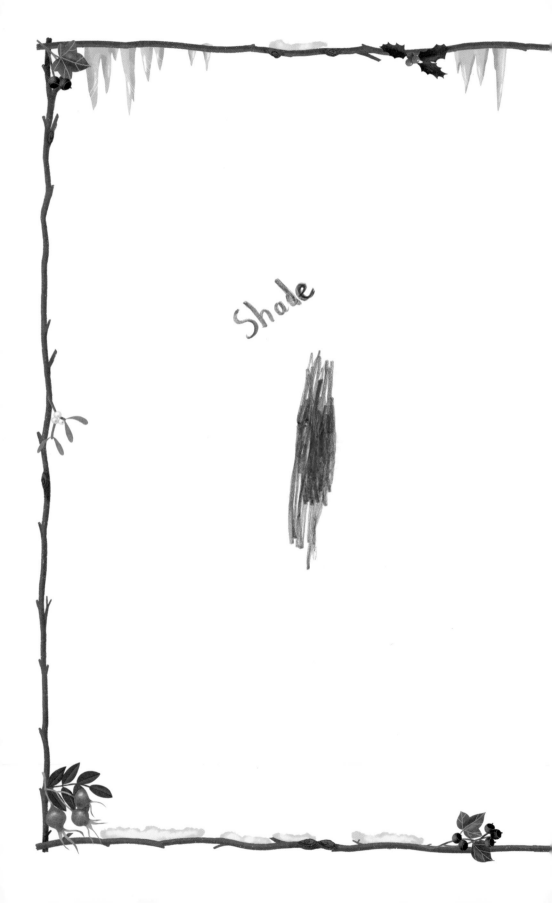

Shade

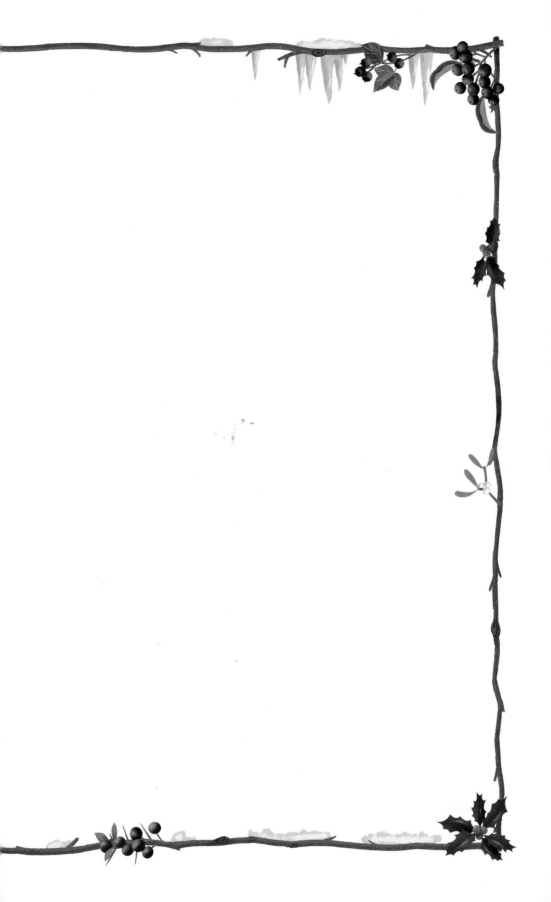

Wisps of silver
Soft as mane
Go back in time
To be happy again

A ray of sun
A drop of rain
Here comes April
Back again

The sun goes down
A purple sky
The forest goes to sleep with pride
And now the owls
May awake
And hunt their way
Back to sleep
Now the sun may rise, again
So the owls till may sleep
Till dawn again

Glittering frost may not be seen
Let the ~~rds~~ icicles drop.
And turn white to green
Let unicorns play
Wild and free
Just wish and dream
For the sparkling green

Shimmershade grows on the Shimmershade tree.
The Dreamtree Kernel grows on the Dreamtree
but first the white must appear in a dream
Let the sun go to sleep
And let the river run dry

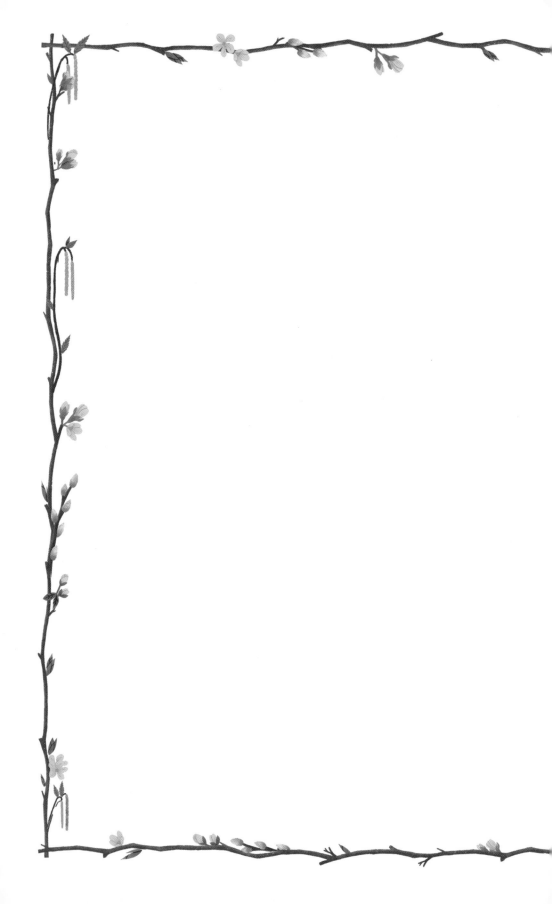

Index